CW00406345

WRITERS REPUBLIC

WHO THE HELL DID I HAVE SEX *With?*

S.O. **MARIE**

Copyright © 2022 by S.O. Marie.

All rights reserved. No part of this book may be reproduced in any form or by any electronic or mechanical means, including information storage and retrieval systems, without permission in writing from the publisher, except by reviewers, who may quote brief passages in a review.

This publication contains the opinions and ideas of its author. It is intended to provide helpful and informative material on the subjects addressed in the publication. The author and publisher specifically disclaim all responsibility for any liability, loss, or risk, personal or otherwise, which is incurred as a consequence, directly or indirectly, of the use and application of any of the contents of this book.

WRITERS REPUBLIC L.L.C.
515 Summit Ave. Unit R1
Union City, NJ 07087, USA

Website: *www.writersrepublic.com*
Hotline: *1-877-656-6838*
Email: *info@writersrepublic.com*

Ordering Information:
Quantity sales. Special discounts are available on quantity purchases by corporations, associations, and others. For details, contact the publisher at the address above.

Library of Congress Control Number: 2022916490
ISBN-13: 979-8-88536-830-8 [Paperback Edition]
979-8-88536-831-5 [Digital Edition]

Rev. date: 08/30/2022

CONTENTS

Introduction vii
Chapter 1 Drip Drop 1
Chapter 2 Neighbors Know My Name 3
Chapter 3 I'll Take You To The Barber Shop! 7
Chapter 4 Small Problems 11
Chapter 5 One Night Stand 13
Chapter 6 Cake It 17
Chapter 7 Giving Back Matters 21
Chapter 8 Colombia 23
Chapter 9 No, He Didn't! 27
Chapter 10 Coffee And Sex In The Morning 31
Chapter 11 Pink Stoner Bum 35
Chapter 12 Entanglement 37

INTRODUCTION

I am sure people have stories about who they had sex with either about how bad it was, weird, or interesting. Some of them are funny, some of them are horrifying and embarrassing, and some is just the best you ever had. This book is about speaking about different types of sexual encounters to readers and showing life lessons to everybody who is relating to these stories. People can relate to these stories and even visualize the type of sex that's going on. This can even give you some new ideas to try in the bedroom with your sex partner. You will laugh, think, relate and visualize. Every sex story has a lesson in the end, so take advice from it.

CHAPTER

1

DRIP DROP

There is just always a good guy you start to date and get to know, and you feel like you're kind of lucky because he treats you like royalty. You got the whole package until the day comes when you decide to sleep with him and then you lose that attraction which sucks ass. I aint gonna lie; he sucked my titties pretty good but the moment he took his hat off, so much sweat was just dripping down all over my body and his Austin Powers chest was just getting too sweaty and sticky! Shit was just disgusting and then I couldn't get over his bald old man looking ass head. I still liked him, but I started to only like him as a friend, but I didn't tell him that. I hated the sex, but I didn't want him to go nowhere because he was a very good guy and I felt close to him. Shit he was the first one to eat the groceries and it was at my sister's graduation. Amazing! But the next problem was him having a small penis.

I never gave him head because it was too small, and the fuckin condoms would always slip in my pussy! Like what the hell bro?

He had to play doctor all the fuckin time sticking 4 fingers in my pussy to find the condom. Every time I was on the bottom and I was grinding on his dick, all I can do is look at his shiny head just sweating. I would tell him to lay back so I wouldn't have to look at his head. I would ride him fast so I can just get my nut off but here we go with the fucking condom slipping in my pussy. I would set the mood by lighting candles, putting lingerie and slowly crawling on him and grabbing his dick to put it in me so I can ride it and even handcuff him to the bed. What the fuck was the point of all that if every night I can't even cum because I got to focus on not getting a small condom slipping in me?

I just ended up cheating on him by dry humping another guy next to some deer's in the woods. Dry humping was better than a sweaty bald head dripping all over my body and condoms always slipping in. I sound super bogus but damn. Mike did call the relationship off and I was sad to be honest. But in all honesty when you're not enjoying sex with somebody and you're not attracted to them the relationship is bound to fail. But hey we weren't meant to be.

LESSON LEARNED: If you're not attracted to somebody, don't string them along. The relationship is bound to fail

CHAPTER

2

NEIGHBORS KNOW MY NAME

You never know who you're going to meet on Facebook. I was speaking to this guy for a whole year and never met him because he lived in Pennsylvania and I was in Chicago. I honestly thought I was being catfished. I finally met with him after a year and I was so happy. He came to Chicago and we met up with each other in the Southside on 63rd street so I was wondering where the hell he was taking me. He had family on 63rd so I didn't mind.

Now may I remind you we in the hood, so what happened in the bedroom was beyond my surprise. I didn't really know how to suck dick at that time, so I didn't understand what was going on. We did a 69 position, so as I'm going down on him I'm hearing him scream my name loud as hell like a damn female. I thought this dude was hood. I didn't even cum when he gave me oral sex because I was laughing. When I decided to just lay on my back He ended up sticking his penis way too deep in my pussy and my period came early, and he was still screaming my name like he was dying. I ran into the bathroom crying not knowing if it's because this shit was embarrassing that my period came or that he may possibly be a woman.

I see guys out the window with guns and weed and looking up and laughing because I guess they thought I was the one who was screaming. I was done after that because I was convinced this dude was a woman.

He went back to Pennsylvania and then I traveled to see him because shit, loneliness gets to you and there was no one available to help me get my nut off. When we had sex, I had a little bit more experience on giving oral sex and after he ate me out in the most wonderful way I figured he deserved everything I learned. So, I started drinking my Stella Rosa wine and I just laid it down by sucking on his neck and dick and then slowly riding him. Next thing you know he went from screaming my name in Chicago to Screaming in Pennsylvania OH MY GOD BABY WHERE THE FUCK YOU LEARNED THIS FROM!! OH MY GOD OH MY GOD IM FINNA CUM AHHHHH!!!! Then 15 seconds later there's a knock-knock on the door and its people asking is everything okay. I wanted to say so bad "No everything is not okay because this dude won't let me cum but gets to be the one to scream."

I can't tell you how many times I felt like there was laughing gas in a room because that's how much I wouldn't stop laughing and getting angry at the same time. I couldn't catch a break, and worst of all I didn't get a chance to cum. Part of me was proud I can make a man scream but the other part was like "is this dude gay, who the fuck screams this loud to the point neighbors got to come over and be like is everything okay, Who's S********? I would ride him like there was no tomorrow and he slapped me thinking I would like it but I slapped his ass back and spit in his mouth while still riding him and having him scream my name.

This dude was seeing so many women behind my back because they all tolerated the fact he was broke and acted like he could star on a show called angry ass women, but he kept coming back to me because I was a freak and there are women who just were too scared to slap him, call him a bitch and spit in his mouth while fucking him. At the end of the day, no matter who he goes to, or how many women he dates he's going to always remember my name and so will his neighbors.

LESSON LEARNED: Don't put your time in someone you gotta always question.

CHAPTER

3

I'LL TAKE YOU TO THE BARBER SHOP!

After I got dumped by my second sex partner, I felt like I needed something new. So, I had this girl I worked with introduce me to her side dude and we pretty much hit it off. I kind of did some sexual stuff with her first like allow her to tongue me down all the way to giving me oral sex. Yes, even as a straight woman I let her eat it because I was horny! She ate it pretty good and licked it all slow and I guess she just felt comfortable enough to introduce me to her side dude. The moment we met up he looked at me straight in my eyes and just wouldn't stop looking, and she didn't like it. Now, Scorpios have a way of hypnotizing people with their eyes and me and this dude were both Scorpios so we both knew what tricks we was going to pull on each other.

I basically cut her off to have a sex relationship with him. She was stalking me because I was at his house everyday and I kept it in my pants for so long because he's a Scorpio, so I had to play with his mind a little bit. The girl was sending me death threats because she was realizing she lost her side dude to a girl who is kind of simple. Months go by and he introduces me to his friends, and they bring this music soundtrack because he was trying to be a rapper. I never got into that kind of life and I was like "Bro you are 30, and your music sucks" stick to the barber shop because that where he worked.

I kept it real with him about his music and part of him hated that but the other part of him loved how blunt and real I was for a simple chick. He took me to his barber shop at nighttime and I'm not going to lie, the Hennessey we drank hit and I was horny as fuck! So, while he was sitting on the barber chair, I took my clothes off and his and got on top of him and took it from there. I pulled his head back, sucked his neck and grabbed his dick and put it in so he can relax. I took it from there and even slapped him around a little bit. We ended up falling on the floor and still going at it and then when he decided to eat me out then all hell really broke loose. I said AWW HELL NAW! Your mouth too dry and its hurting me! Who the fuck has a tongue that hurts a pussy?

Right when I was about to run away from that shit, somebody came right on time and walked in on us and saying his song didn't have a hit and I was just like" You are not a rapper". I even said this while I'm naked in a barbershop in front of a stranger so that's how serious I was. He even went out of town and apparently fucked a bunch of women because he thought he was famous. This dude never had one song on the radio and believed he was famous. So, because he fucked a bunch of women thinking he was famous I end up with a STD. I have never had a STD before, so I was pissed and scared, I thought I was going to die. I never heard of Chlamydia at that time but hey I found out it was curable, so I didn't take it seriously.

I broke his windows and stole all his weed he planted because as a Scorpio, I'm very vengeful. You don't give me a STD and then disappear and say I'm the one who gave it to you. His rapper money was coming from selling weed, so I took all the damn plants and smoked that shit and even sold it. Till this day I have never heard his music on the radio. Bro you 40 now!!!

Lesson Learned: Don't fuck with no wannabe rapper who isn't going anywhere in life and will have no issue giving you a STD. Receiving some head is relaxing but a dry tongue burning you is not.

CHAPTER 4

SMALL PROBLEMS

I had a crush on this guy for 10 years. He was handsome as hell and I love a man with dreads and nappy hair. I was so obsessed with him since I was 10. After all these years I finally get him and I'm happy as hell. Only problem with him is he wouldn't take me out nowhere. His ass would only invite me to his messy ass house to drink and smoke. I even had to buy my own alcohol.

I'm not going to lie, I was feeling some type of way and always said to myself what the fuck am I doing here. But I would still go to his house and sleep over because it's been a while since a guy asked me to sleep over without giving him some so, I found that kind of nice for a while. I heard a lotta things about him such as the way how he's amazing in bed and can lift a girl up and know how to work his dick. So, I'm a bit tipsy and he had just got his dreads re done and that shit made me horny as hell. I just started pulling it and pushed him to the wall, bit his lip and licked all his muscles and he took his pants off and mine. Then he turned off the light and I'm wondering if he's just laying against me, grinding without putting it in so I put my hand under and I'm thinking he's trying to finger me because I feel his thumb.

The lights accidently got turned on and then I look down and saw his penis. In my mind I'm like aw shit that shit is small no wonder I didn't feel anything. I had it in my mind that he would be packing, but I was young and stupid at the time. I ran in the bathroom and had to think do I want to fuck him, or should I go home? I still loved how he looked with the dreads, so I just said fuck it. Then I laid back on his bed with some lingerie and he shoved it in till the point my wig came off! And I'm like what the fuck I'm starting to get cramps down there with this small dick, and my wig cap is out in the open. How the fuck is this baby dick hurting the fuck out of me and made my wig fall on the floor.

So many women have said he's amazing in bed but shit I couldn't relate to anything they said.

I've dealt with a tiny dick before, so I gave it a chance by continuing to go to his house to have sex with him, riding him, licking him and pulling his dreads but I never felt anything in my pussy unless he was shoving it in, and that shit made me burn everytime I would pee.

As I continued to see him, I thought to myself; this man has a baby dick and still isn't taking me out? Aw hell naw! I just finally dipped. The dreads were no longer working on me.

Lesson learned: Just because you love the way someone looks, if he isn't taking you out and you can't even enjoy him inside you, it isn't worth sticking around.

CHAPTER

5

ONE NIGHT STAND

You know how you're physically attracted to someone, but he is always in a relationship so you're never able to get a chance? This dude was that person. He loved only dark-skinned women, so I was not the type of person he was crazy about. I knew him for 5 years and just never got the chance. I honestly never cared if I wasn't somebody's type I always got what I wanted. I'm a Scorpio and I got hypnotic eyes so of course I never failed at getting what I wanted. My self-catch phrase was always "look into my eyes and you will be sucked in".

So, one year he got this girl pregnant and I honestly didn't like her. She just gave me negative vibes and was always a hater. He never wanted me, so bitch what the fuck are you rolling your eyes for? Dark skin women are so beautiful and sexy to me, but this bitch looked like a sea donkey because of her attitude. Her personality was just so ugly to me.

One day I guess she was 6 months pregnant and he invited me over because for some reason he wanted to talk to me at his house. I was drinking a margarita because I was never his type so why the hell would I see him sober, and why is he trying talk to me at his crib? I honestly took the chance to fuck him. I laid him down, pored some liquor on his chest and was slowly licking it off and got on top and put his dick in my pussy. I was slowly riding it and then went a little faster. He was for real liking it and was saying "damn you must have been waiting for this for a long time".

I honestly didn't look down at his dick when I got on top, and when I finally did, he said "don't even think about saying anything." He said that because his dick was small and lighter than I was use to but I didn't care. He ate my pussy like he was eating a whole ass watermelon. After we were done, I decided to spend the night.

This mother fucker took all the covers and just wouldn't give me nothing not even a fuckin sheet or a pillow. After he fell asleep, I just picked up my heels and tip toed out his door. That was my first one-night stand and it honestly wasn't bad in my mind. I waited so long to fuck him and got what I wanted because that's just me. I never wanted to see him again, but I patted myself on the back and walked home because I just needed sex. Even though I had to walk 2 hours back to my house I still patted myself and said Score! Then next thing I know I am hearing from a bunch of people how his baby mama wants to beat me up because she saw me leaving his house in the morning time looking like I was doing the walk of shame. Even though I was, I continued to say that wasn't me, that was another mixed chick. But at the end of the day me and him were single and I got what I wanted but will never do it with someone like him again. It really wasn't worth the drama

Lesson Learned: There is nothing wrong with a one-night stand, just don't have one with someone who has a crazy baby mama and won't even be a gentlemen in the bedroom.

CHAPTER 6

CAKE IT

After everything I been through with the wrong guys I dated, all the crying, and depression, I just gave up for a while and decided to start drinking so I went to the liquor store and I ran into this dude who. wasn't really my type but he told me for years he's been trying to get my attention, but I continued giving him fake numbers since I was 15. But I didn't remember shit about him, and I thought this dude was crazy, annoying and a creep. But even though I thought about all that I said, "Fuck it." I was lonely and needed some fun with a new guy, so I gave him my number.

I got to know him and kind of liked him because we were always talking at the beach in the sunset and relaxing without him asking to fuck. Then one day I just said to myself "he can have this pussy." The moment I gave it to him, he just started to show his asshole side, but I continued fucking with him anyways. Then I said to myself, I'ma show this dude why he shouldn't think about losing me, so I waited till his birthday to give him what I call a birthday special. The birthday special is giving a man the best sex of his life to the point where his legs are shaking, and getting him to scream my name. Happy Birthday!!

I put on some sexy all white with lace lingerie, you know almost as if he was looking at a Victoria Secret angel model. When he actually seen me all he could say was "damn" while licking his big ol' juicy lips." I proceeded to get on top of him, I laid him down, and had a little round cake with a candle for him to blow it out. After he blew it out, I put all the cake on him from top to bottom and I slowly licked the cake off from his neck, his abs, and I put more cream on his dick and put the whole thing in my mouth and deep throated him until all the cream and cake was off. All he could do was scream "aw fuck, this shit was so damn good". His legs begin to lock up, and yes my name was said. I did a second round on sucking his dick till it got super wet so I can slip it in easier and ride it. We end up falling asleep until the next morning.

As time went on, we would start arguing like a married couple even in public. Then one day the most awkward embarrassing argument happened. I got invited to his family party and they are telling him how much they like me, and he must stop being stupid.

This jackass decides to say in front of everybody "She ain't all that, I do all the work in the bedroom." I'm thinking "Ight I'ma blast this dude" So I said, "You say you do all the work but who was the one screaming my name?" Everybody spit out their beer and started cracking up and he really tried hard for a comeback and said "Hold up I don't be screaming her name, there was a time she put cake on my dick but that's all." I said "you still be screaming my name and all the guys dropped their jaws and said "Did you say she put cake on your Johnson and licked it all off and you complaining? I just walked out because only a clown would embarrass me like that. Especially putting our sex life on blast.

Now may I remind you once again, I'ma Scorpio so I'm very vengeful when I feel I have been wronged. I knew how to get my revenge on his ass. I hit him up and asked can I come over because I know he misses my sex. So, I went over got some wine and Hennessey and after I drank my wine, I sucked the shit out his dick, I spit on it and deep throated till I took his soul. He was screaming so I got on top of him and was riding him till he said, "I love you." After he said that I said "say it again and then I spit in his mouth. I left his house and the next day he was saying "Damn baby, last night was just amazing, I love you." After those words were said I said "Now you can tell your family you lost the girl who gave you the best sex of your life." I am a boss bitch and nobody talks shit about the way I fuck in the bedroom.

Lesson Learned: DON'T WASTE YOUR TIME WITH SOMEONE WHO DOESN'T VALUE YOU.

CHAPTER

7

GIVING BACK MATTERS

College can get stressful to the point you desperately need a stress reliever. Dealing with family, friends, and studying everyday all day makes you want to fuck somebody to get some stress out. I needed some dick and it wasn't hard to figure out who to do it with. There was this dude Mike and he was sexy as fuck. He had a six pack and nappy hair and nappy hair is irresistible to me. One interesting thing about him was that he was mysterious and obviously that's a Scorpio thing. Even though he had these positive traits his ass was the type to never leave his house and just watch TV all day, drink and smoke because he feared the outside world.

That was weird as hell, but his sexy body made up for it, so I was still fucking him with no strings attached. It was easy to not catch feelings and just have him as a fuck buddy. He was a Scorpio, so I'm expecting him to be a complete freak, but this dude didn't even eat pussy. We would only do quickies, so it never came to a point where we did oral sex on each other.

The moment I decided to suck him up to the point he screamed my name I am expecting the same shit in return but nope! He didn't even look or second guess about eating my pussy and I got extremely pissed off. I said "First of all, you scared to go outside and live life and now you're telling me you can't eat my pussy? AW HELL NAW IM OUT! I drank a lotta Hennessey and I was controlling myself from throwing up because I was being courteous. Because I couldn't get back what I gave, I threw up on his ass and all over his window and TV. I probably was petty for that but damn I wanted some head so I was mad because I couldn't get pleased like I deserved. I am a pleaser and a freak and I demand to get that in return.

After I threw up everywhere, I went out the door and said "this could have been prevented if you would have just ate my pussy bro." Good luck cleaning all this up."

Lesson Learned: WHAT YOU GIVE, ALWAYS MAKE SURE YOU GET THE SAME THING IN RETURN

CHAPTER 8

COLOMBIA

Now when you leave the state it's a perfect time to live your single life to the fullest. I went to Colombia with my mom for a two-week vacation and man…. I had some good vacation sex. My mom was once married to someone who got deported to Colombia and that's who we stayed with. I have his last name, but I have never met him before, and it was kind of nice meeting him. Now before I go further, He is not my father, and he is not the one I had a sex encounter with. So anyways, he introduced me to his sons and then I just couldn't stop staring at his middle son Antonio who was about 28 but he was married.

My mom decided to get a big cabin for all of us to stay in and then it was an experience I can't forget. Antonio decided to take me for a motorcycle ride while his wife was getting to know my mom and that motorcycle ride really got me horny. Nobody thought anything about a moto cycle ride because everybody in Colombia rides motorcycles and there's always someone in the back. In Colombia even women with heels will give a man a ride on a motorcycle. That ride made me like him a lot and horny as fuck because riding around a country I never been before was an adventure and it was just exciting exploring this place with a sexy man. I went to sleep so happy when we returned.

My mom and her ex-husband made this a family trip where him, his sons, me and my mom would go everywhere together even Antonio's wife. He would not stop staring at me and I felt his vibe to the point I stayed wet every time we locked eyes. Then one day we were all in a cabin where there was different bathrooms and bedrooms being connected. I had a room where there was a big window and it was also next to Antonio and his wife's room. I took a nap and he popped up from my window and grabbed my face and kissed me and it was just shocking he risked doing that while his wife was in the other room. He told me to come outside from the window and he grabbed me, sucked on my neck, pulled my pants down and just sucked the shit out my pussy to the point I was shaking, and I just had to leave and get back through the window and lock it because I was ready to fuck the shit out him but I couldn't see myself doing something with a married guy

I saw my mom talking all happy with Antonio after we came back inside and sat on the couch and in my mind, I am saying to myself "mom, I wouldn't be too happy talking to him and in his face if I were you." The next morning everybody was asleep and then he sneaks in my room and just starts slowly eating me out. His tongue was so soft just going round and round and I felt like my soul was coming out my body and I was in another world. He poured liquor in my mouth and I just started saying "damelo, damelo." He only spoke Spanish and all I did was speak English, so I just figured I might as well say a lil something in Spanish for him to understand. I spit on his dick and sucked so hard without even choking, and he's just grabbing my neck and biting the shit out of me. I am not gonna lie, my soul was taken and we didn't even begin to fuck. Then we hear his wife and he jumps out the window and I hide under the covers because I'm naked and he left his clothes and he's outside naked and I throw him his clothes and he gets in the bedroom with his wife and said he was drinking outside.

That was a good and funny experience for me, and I was expecting that to happen again but involving actual fucking, but it never did. I was upset the rest of my vacation because his wife kept giving me dagger eyes and would grab his dick in front of me. I had to remind myself this is her husband and she's just trying to show me he's hers and I get it. I still didn't regret what I did because it was the best head experience of my life and like I said when you leave the state it's a perfect time to live your single life to the fullest and what happens in Colombia stays in Colombia.

Lesson Learned: Be careful fuckin with a married man on vacation

CHAPTER

9

NO, HE DIDN'T!

You know when you're in a relationship and it's just not fun anymore? Your boyfriend pays no attention to you and you just want excitement and since your boyfriend is not giving it to you, you might decide it to get excitement from someone else! Hey, call it hoe behavior or whatever you want but I am only human and it's nice to get male attention and some dick every now and then. So, while my so-called boyfriend was ghosting me, I just decided to get a gym membership to rub off all the negative feelings I had. The moment I walked in LA Fitness so many male staff were giving me so much attention and everybody was white and cute, but I noticed this Carmel chocolate tall guy and I love me some chocolate tall people.

I sat by his desk, gave him straight eye contact, smiled and slowly said, "can you help me setup a membership and with a low price." And of course, he said yes so, I started to go to the gym everyday to talk to him and as time went by, he straight up said "please let me be your sugar daddy." Now that shit was funny to me because I wasn't trying to fuck him, and I am definitely not the type to be messing around with someone just to get some money, so I just insisted on saying let's just have fun for free. 1st time we had sex we went to his apartment and it was small as hell and all cluttered up and in my mind I'm thinking to myself how the fuck is this man trying to be a sugar daddy when this place looks like a damn teenage trap house. But I let it slide.

He started kissing and licking on my tattoo on the back of my neck and I laid him down on the bed and ripped his LA fitness shirt off and licked all over his neck and stomach and flipped me over so fast and just put it in. We had some pretty good sex even though it was pretty quick and simple. Since the sex was good, I went to his house for the second time, but this motherfucker fell asleep while I was riding him, and he already came but I didn't! I thought I killed his ass or some shit because he went to a deep sleep and wouldn't wake up and I was disappointed when I checked his pulse and he was alive and then started snoring. What fuckin man randomly falls asleep while his dick is in a damn vagina. I just got off him and then a text popped up on his phone saying" I hate being married to you, you're a fuckin cheating ass bitch, I am getting full custody of our son."

That was my queue to punch his face and take his shoes and dip. Crazy part about all this was he knew who my boyfriend was after I found out about his wife, so this shit was big time KARMA for my ass. A couple years go by and we run into each other and just laugh about the past and hit it off. Once again, I haven't had any D in a while, so I was willing to get my needs met. 2 days later the moment I was deciding to get my needs met I see his ass on the Maury show and the episode was called "I'm the candy man." And he's on there as a cheating boyfriend and I am Like aww hell naw!!!

This man surprises me every single time and the fact that this show came up the moment I was deciding to fuck him was pretty scary but luckily, I mastered the art of masturbation, so I blocked his ass and seduced myself and came. That was it and I just realized this dude gives me crazy ass experiences and it's just god's way of saying "no not him." I took that with me everytime

Lesson Learned: Don't fuck another guy when you got a boyfriend because Karma is real!

CHAPTER

10

COFFEE AND SEX IN THE MORNING

When you wake up from a long drunken night with a sexy person it can be nice. What makes it even more nice is when they ask you do you want breakfast? I went to New York for my birthday because I have family members there and I especially go to see my grandma. When I went to see my grandma in Manhattan, she had a fancy apartment who had a guard in the lobby. He was fine as hell. He had everything I always find sexually attractive; muscles, abs, tattoos everywhere, chocolate skin, nappy hair, and the type that speaks all sultry. By sultry I mean hot, charming, smooth and sexy as hell.

I honestly wouldn't think someone like that would be into me because I had self-esteem issues and this man was just too good to be true. His name was Keith and the first thing that comes to mind about him is Keith Sweat singing the song "Nobody" Because let me tell you, compared to everybody I dated, Nobody could compare to him look wise and smooth wise. His looks, his charm and voice was just everything I was looking for in a man. The day He asked me out, we slept together later that night because I only had 3 days in New York to celebrate my birthday and I needed birthday Sex. We were in a closed coffee shop because he told me he owned it and wanted me to check it out.

We went in and he pushed me to the table and ripped my clothes off and handcuffed me to the table. He started licking and sucking my neck and pulled my hair and just started licking from top to bottom and of course ate my pussy out so slowly and I cum fast when I am receiving oral sex. But he made sure that didn't happen. I'm trying to fuck him and grab him but damn, both my hands are handcuffed to the table what the fuck am I supposed to do? I'm getting horny as fuck and I'm trying to get off the table to ride his dick, but this mf wouldn't uncuff me.

Now I know I should be feeling grateful that a man is trying to please me but I'm for real trying to ride his dick and enjoy myself but he tells me "No you're not getting off this table" and he just continues to eat my pussy and then says "This is too good don't move" but I can't even fuckin move. In my mind I was thinking this was hot in the beginning but damn I can't fuckin move and I am wondering if this man plans on killing me the way this whole setting is looking. My legs are shaking while my arms are hurting and for some fuckin reason he's making sure I don't cum.

All I could think was how I don't believe I will be getting my nut off for my birthday tonight. Turns out he never wanted me to cum. He told me "this is what I do" I honestly started to feel like I might be getting held hostage and this might be the day I die because I was cuffed to the table till the next morning. This was not the type of birthday sex I was expecting. After he uncuffed me he made his so called special coffee and gave me a cup and then said “this was fun” I told him “Bro I felt like you was gonna kill me, I didn’t even get to ride your dick and I especially didn’t cum so How the hell was this fun? He told me” you didn’t need to cum” and then drank a cup of coffee and then said I’m finna open my store soon.

I took his ‘coffee and said “ this coffee tastes horrible and needs extra sweet cream” Of course, he got mad, but I told him “ this was a 15 hour tease” I couldn’t even tell myself if that was the best or weirdest or worst experience of my life. I got my pussy ate pretty good, but my vagina couldn’t even move or cum. I still till this day can’t explain what kind of experience that was. Just know it was him if a woman got killed in a coffee shop.

LESSON LEARNED: Keep your eyes open, sexy people can be the devil

CHAPTER 11

PINK STONER BUM

Man, when I say desperate times calls for desperate measures this was some most definite desperate shit. When I don't have sex for almost a year, I go insane. I can't think, I can't sleep and all I can do is have wet dreams and wake up disappointed it wasn't real life. While I was in college, I ran into someone I went to elementary school with and he was one of the cool guys. He was also white, and people know that don't always fall into my category of sex partners. Not to be racist I just never experienced being with a white guy.

He was looking kind of cute and I honestly wasn't having any male attention and it was fun getting to know him as man instead of a 10-year-old elementary kid. John was just interesting to be around because like I said I'm not a vanilla type of person. I finally went to his house and we smoked weed and drank and when I drink my pussy is just screaming "Time to fuck" I guess he read my mind and just started sucking on my titties because that's my weakest spot. I'm bound to fuck or dry hump a person quick as hell who sucks on my titties and kisses my neck.

We were on his couch when he did all this. I took his pants off so I can ride him but the moment I saw his penis I just couldn't do it. It was all pink and looked like a small balloon you can just easily pop. It was just something I never saw before. I just took a step back, but my pussy was still screaming because I'm drunk so I just close my eyes and tell him to stick it in. He was doing a pretty good job and even though my eyes were closed I was still grinding like there was no tomorrow because 1. I haven't had sex in almost a year, and 2. My pussy becomes a waterfall when I'm drunk, and I have the urge to fuck. He pulled my hair so I choked him, and then when he tried to turn me around the couch, it broke down. We were drunk and high so we kept it going like it was nothing.

I came, so I got off and was like this wasn't bad at all. But 3 days later I find out he has no job, no independence, and just does nothing but smoke weed and forget to tell females he has a girlfriend. I got pissed the fuck off because I don't have sex with people who have girlfriends and the fact this this white ass bum had somebody, I exploded and broke all his bongs. I shouldn't have gotten mad over a bum but damn I gave my pussy to this pink dick motherfucker. I still had to move forward and be like at least I'm good for another couple months, meaning I am no longer sexually frustrated, and I can deal with not having sex for a bit. This shit still wasn't cool and now I for sure won't have the decency to give a white boy a chance.

LESSON LEARNED: Sometimes you dont get what you want and can get dissapointed when your desperate to get your nut off

CHAPTER

12

ENTANGLEMENT

Now there is a reason this is the last chapter and you will understand once you finish reading. This is the lesson of all lessons. First let me start of by saying is if you know the Jada Pinkett Smith and August Alsina story then I am letting you know that I am August in this story. This sex story I am about to discuss came with the very beginning of COVID-19 and the new word entanglement. If you know what was going on during the 1st year of COVID-19 then you know single people had a little struggle finding new ass.

I finally got a good job after I finished getting my social work degree and the moment COVID-19 started to get serious I just decided to take a chance on a coworker. He was Nigerian and a basketball player and fine. All the women at my job wanted him and I took my time to just take my shot at him. Hell, I even started asking him can I suck his dick because he was a gentleman and honestly was the type of guy I would please any day. This was just supposed to be a sex thing but it just turned into something more. I honestly had a good experience because I have never met a sexy man who was a gentleman and just always made sure I was good and never made me feel bad about myself.

My only issue was I just felt like this was too good to be true. Also, he was a Gemini and I was so obsessed about how long I can make things last with him since I never lasted more than 2 months with a Gemini because they are two people in one and can never make up their damn mind. But I continued to see him. Every time we had sex, I made sure I gave him the best head he ever received and the best I ever gave because this type of man really deserved it at the time. I deep throated his dick and put his balls in my mouth and would just suck till I made his mouth open and moan. This was the first guy I would just enjoy sucking on. I asked him all the time can I suck his dick and would tell him how much I miss it and I just enjoyed the sex and this certain bond I felt. I told him I am the type to make a man scream my name and he didn't believe it but once I spit on his dick and put the whole thing in my mouth while putting my hands around his throat, he didn't scream it but he definitely said it so slowly while he started to cum in my mouth, so SCORE!

Then one day he just felt the need to give me head. It was very unexpected because I didn't even think he ate pussy since I was always the one going down. I came so fast I saw his mouth and mustache soaked and it just got me turned on even more. He ended up saying "I just wanted you to be the one to relax this time." I can honestly say I really felt like I finally made love to someone, but it just wasn't that. We would have sex nice and slow and I just felt like I was in an Usher song singing "Aint gotta rush, I just wanna take it nice and slow." We would always say to each other "I'ma fuck you so hard and rough." but it just always turned out nice and slow.

Him licking my body and me licking all over his and just switching positions. I was feeling good about him moaning because I just love when I make a man moan. He would even spend the night at my house and we would cuddle like were together. I can honestly say I started to like him more than I have ever did anybody else. I just enjoyed riding him all slow and sucking his dick till I made him open his mouth and moan. I would always lick all over his muscles, behind his ear and down to his dick and we would just literally choke each other out. I held his neck and he held mine while we were fucking because it was all about both of us taking control. I always called his ass daddy even when we fucked. When I got on top, I would ride him good and be like "Come on daddy, whose dick is this." and of course he would moan and say "This dick is yours it's all yours." When he would flip me over to my back, I just always made sure I scratched his back so hard so my mark can be on him and let him know his ass belongs to me. He really took my freaky side out and just made me feel so good because I had self-esteem issues with my body.

I felt like I just wasn't his type because he was so fit and I was a little chubby with no flat stomach but he just always told me he loved my body and the more he said that the more I fell for him and just made the mistake of trying to rush things and be obsessive about if he sees himself going further with me. Unfortunately, I forgot that this was just a sex thing. I felt hurt that I let myself get too caught up in the moment and completely forgot what this was. I just never been treated good by a man and this is what made me fall for him because this was a new experience of being treated like a queen. This is the last chapter because every single chapter was about the wrong men I had sex with. These men were garbage and they just weren't the people I deserved, nor did they deserve me.

This sex relationship only lasted for a short period of time because I fucked it up, but in all honesty, it just wasn't meant to be. Turns out he was just one of those Nigerians that people warn you about being the most charming, having the most money, treating women wonderful but having more than one woman. This was a lesson to know not to shit where you eat but also I am worthy of a good man, I deserve to be treated like a queen, and I am enough and no more giving my body up to people who don't deserve someone like me. Even though I have made plenty mistakes in my life because I am only human, I am a very beautiful and phenomenal woman and I am worthy and deserve true love and I finally know what I am looking for in someone. Even though I got caught up in the sheets and fell for someone who I knew wasn't trying to be in a relationship, I want to thank him even though he would have the mind power to have a significant other slap another person at the Oscars. (It wasn't your fault Will Smith)

There were times I hated this man and allowed myself to be mindfucked because he just stopped fucking with me because I made a mistake as a fucking human being. At the end of the day I learned something that I should have learned my whole life and that I should have been realizing after every bad sex encounter I had, and that is I am worthy of a good man, I am worthy of love, I am worthy to be happy, I am just WORTHY PERIOD! I am not going to say his name but all I can say is even though this was an entanglement, I've never felt more valuable about myself than I do now. THANK YOU O! And to Will Smith, you are worthy bro!! No more getting mindfucked!!

Whoever finis hed this book "You are worthy" If you're going to have sex with someone, make sure they truly deserve to have your body.

Lightning Source UK Ltd.
Milton Keynes UK
UKHW041319050323
418057UK00001B/62

9 798885 368308